NOT FAR FROM THE JUNCTION

(21 May 2019)

A novelette

WILL ASHON

OPEN PEN

First Published in 2020
by Open Pen, 25 Crescent Road, London, E13 0LU
openpen.co.uk
9781916413696
OPNOV007

OPEN PEN NOVELETTES #6
"Not Far From The Junction"
First Edition

not far from the junction

(21 May 2019)

1. Andrew
2. Michael
3. Arno
4. Kirsten
5. Gary
6. Vij
7. Jason
8. Mahir
9. Ryan, *Emma* & **Pip**

1.

I'm heading up to H_____ to go and see my girlfriend.

I'm a struggling actor and I'm struggling so badly that most of the time I haven't got any work at all.

Exactly, so I'm making the most of not having anything to do by going somewhere else.

Anything I can do is the honest answer to that. I mean, I'd love to do more theatre work, that'd be fantastic. My dream ever since I was a kid was to be at the RSC, but it's difficult enough to get into acting, let alone getting on to the stage at the RSC!

2.

I've just dropped the wife off at the airport. She's on her way to X. She comes from X and we are in the process of selling our house in C______ and moving to X and she is going to basically put her parents' minds at rest that I can manage the thing. [laughs]

3.

Well, originally E______, North London.

Four years.

Cheaper property. Yeah. Crazy. I still got relatives in London so I know what house prices are like up there. It's crazy.

4.

I'll be brutally honest with you, I've never picked up a hitchhiker before in my life, I just took one quick glance at you, you looked like a decent guy, you've only got a backpack, you looked like you needed a hand.

I just saw you and I thought you looked like
you were in need.

I'm actually just going to the Post Office
to pick up a letter but yeah, we can stop
wherever you need to stop.

We could do that for you, yeah.

This isn't a route I normally take so that was a
purely chance meeting.

5.

Like I say, I can probably take you quite a fair
way cos I'll go in back end of N______ and
drop you off a few extra junctions.

I always tend to stop, to be fair. If somebody
needs help why not help them? And I'd like
to think that if I was having to hitchhike
somewhere that somebody'd pick me up. I

always think, *If I'm going that way, why not?* Like I say, I hope I don't get raped and murdered one day but so far I've been lucky! [laughs]

6.

I don't like to see people struggling, basically. You know what I mean? I'm going this way, I've got a four, five seater car, you look pretty okay, you don't look like you're gonna pull a knife out and stab me, so…!

You know, it was the on-your-knees-with-your-hands-clasped that gave it away really! [laughs]

7.

I'm going to D______, mate, if that's any good?

I've just finished work and I'm going home.

I do white-lining. Road markings.

Don't know if I'm honest. I've never picked anyone up before. I'm always in lorry when I see people. And I always said I'd stop but it's got cameras in so I'm not allowed like.

Yeah, every day.

Yeah, it's a nightmare at this time.

8.

I was going for an interview actually.

Average. It's not my best interview. It's one of the first interviews I've done in like seven years.

Got made redundant a couple of months ago. So I'm out of work.

9.

What it is today, we're travelling down from M____ to L_____shire to collect a… what is it now?

A trailer tent.

Trailer tent.

•

1.

No. When I was at school I wanted to be a marine biologist. Academically I was too lazy, so after a few years of bouncing around the country trying to figure out what I was gonna do, I ended up working in IT. And that was quite a good fit. I was an IT technician till I was 44. But that was when my marriage fell apart and I thought, *Okay, so now what? I'm stuck in a job that I ended up hating.* So I quit, I went travelling. I worked in Y on a marine conservation project for a couple of months, which was fulfilment of a dream. Got back, thought, *What do I do now?*

Ooh, I know, I've always enjoyed acting. Fuck it, I'll give it a go. See if I can do it. So I got on to an acting course in London, completed that and graduated and have had two jobs in the last two years! [laughs]

That's two more than some, yeah! Exactly. Exactly.

2.

I was in the restaurant business in London for twenty eight years, got made redundant last year and I'm actually a chauffeur at the moment. I've spent a year chauffeuring and realised that, although the turnover's great, by the time you get down to bottom line it's absolutely nothing. Do I really want to spend the next fifteen years of my existence driving up and down the motorway? We're kind of at a juncture in our lives, like a fork in the road, and we're deciding that we're gonna live a completely different life, right in the middle of the countryside in X. Gonna go back to nature and maybe open some kind of plant food kitchen and give the kids a different perspective on life. Although they're both—I've got a six year old and a nine year old—and they're both fluent in the language already, so the only one the language has a problem with is me.

3.

I got two daughters, 24 and 22. I better not say too much, they can listen on my dash cam!

If they got hold of the memory card out of it they could.

4.

I am in P____________, yeah. I have been here six years, I moved up from S_____.

No, financial reasons. Yeah, very, very expensive

in S_____. My children were 24 and 19 and it was time to think about them gaining independence, basically. They weren't going to be able to do it in S_____.

7.

Where you aiming for?

This is just research for a book is it?

You're brave.

I've never done it. I always said I would, just to see what it were like.

8.

I worked for ________ previously. And they kind of imploded. It went from two thousand staff down to one hundred and fifty, got bought out and then, when they got bought out, that one hundred and fifty went down to less than fifty. So that's where we're at.

Pretty much. It happens every time. They get inspected, audited, the audit didn't go very well, so from there on it changes. It's hard to get back out the rut. But that's me at the moment.

I've managed to take a month out, get some rest, start my own company, get a holiday, and get back on it.

Yeah I hope so. There's always better candidates, but I hope so.

9.

It costs nothing to be nice.

No, bloody hell. Well that's it. They'll look at you, laff, and carry on.

We're old fashioned. If someone's had an

house fire, today's generation, they'll get their phones out, they'll start recording. Whereas, it don't cost nothing to get your arse in there and try and help. Do you know what I mean?

It's not many people who'd help out like us. If we see someone there struggling, even cars and stuff, a'n't we, loads of times, we pull over and help.

Pull over, help them fix the car, and back on your way.

•

2.

She came to England about seventeen years ago. She came to England after she was working for a diplomat in the Z. She came to England to improve her English. She just planned to stay here for a year. And she met me and I obviously put a major spanner in the works. She's sacrificed a lot for me.

We moved to C________ nine years ago. I'm from C________ originally. Part of X-ian culture is to stay at home with the kids until they've finished their first year at school, which my youngest daughter has now done. But being at home for nine years, that has a bit of an impact on your self-confidence. Chuck a bit of Brexit in on top as well and she's feeling like the country doesn't love her anymore. So we're just at that fork in the road and deciding what we wanna do with the rest of our lives. I've certainly changed a lot over the last couple of years. And, you know, looking for a fresh challenge. The challenge of facing the motorway for the next fifteen years doesn't really inspire me a great deal.

4.

It's gonna be tough isn't it? It's gonna be tough.

Let's hope I start off a good day for you.

How have you been getting around then?

And in the name of research, why not? It can be exciting, it can be dangerous, it can be connections that you never knew were gonna happen. It can be many, many things.

5.

As you can tell by the monotonal accent I'm from _____shire. So born and bred in B_______, now live in N__________.

Unfortunately, the children have lost their _____shire accents. We sometimes have to send them back up to't grandparents just so they can get a little bit of a _____shire twang back in them. B________'s always gonna be my hometown, but it's always been a very poor

area of the country, not a lot of investment, and
N________ was just a better lifestyle, really,
for the kids and the family.

Different. Very, very, very, very different. I've got a lot of diverse friends—Asian, Muslim, English etcetera. My best friend's a Sikh. But growing up in B________ there was a lot of racism. I'm ashamed to say that my parents are still of that nature, grandparents are the same. They had bad thoughts of the immigration coming in, especially from the Pakistani community. And obviously we had the riots and things during the time that I was growing up and it seemed to be a bit segregated. There's still a bit of that going on but I'm about as far from being racist as I possibly can. I enjoy the company of anybody—White, Black, Greek, Asian, don't make a difference to me.

6.

Yeah, N_____ born and bred. My dad came over from India when he was nineteen and then settled there, went to XYZ bearings factory. He's actually a jazz musician. Yeah, he's 87 and still playing.

He plays guitar. He's played all his life. He taught himself and yeah, he's really good. He plays keyboard now because his fingers are not so nimble as they used to be.

He was nineteen. And he met my mum. I think they got married about 1958. And I was born in '59.

Yeah, he was self-taught. I don't know what the state of the guitar was like. It was probably a self-made thing.

As I say, he's still playing. He's 87. He's a bit of a John Lee Hooker, you know. My hero. He's got the oldest roadie in town, cos I have to take all his gear for him and I'm 60. [laughs]

He don't do long distance stuff now. He plays at a hotel once a month and he'll probably do a couple of weddings and stuff.

8.

Mum and Dad did their thing and we as kids looked after ourselves, to be honest. Mum and Dad spent most of their time looking after the business and trying to get money into them, into the family, trying to put food on the table. Which worked alright, they've done alright, they're happily retired now. So yeah, in terms of the family, everyone's successful—ish! Two of my sisters have their own business, my brother's in computer software contracting, so he's doing really well. And there's myself at the moment that's just starting again.

•

1.

It's horrific, yeah. I'm in a very lucky position whereby I've got a bit of money behind me so I haven't had to work. I can spend all of my time saying, *I'm gonna be an actor, I'm gonna apply for acting jobs and if it's not an acting job I'm not gonna do it.* But I've got friends of mine who are working fifty, sixty hours a week just to live in London and they also have to be available all the time, at any time, for casting. I dunno how they do it, I really don't.

It's vicious. It's a really brutal industry. And y'know, you've gotta have skin as thick as a rhino to do it. And the most important thing is not to care about rejection. If you're worried about getting rejection? Worst possible thing you can do!

2.

Originally I trained as a chef in C_______. And back in the late '80s there was not really any kind of restaurant scene going on in C_______ so you had to go to London. I'd already been dazzled by the bright lights at 11, 12 years old when me Dad took me. He had to drop something off in Piccadilly and took me there and I got a bit dazzled by the lights, wanted to go to London.

I was always hungry as a kid! Constantly hungry. And whatever I was fed, I always wanted more. I spent a lot of time with my nan where she taught me how to cook and she would fill my stomach for me and that never really left. You know, also, '80, '81, parents getting divorced, it's kind of a bit of a messy divorce, so that disrupted education and so I didn't really do very well at school. But I was pretty good with food, so I sorta stayed with food and went to college and moved to London.

3.

Dry-lining. Plasterboarding.

Working on ten thousand houses just over near where I picked you up. I think that'll see me out, somehow.

They've only done about seven, eight hundred so far. It's massive. Yeah, near B__ H___ there.

4.

I'm on a completely different journey. I'm on a spiritual journey and mine encompasses helping people in need at the moment.

5.

I'm pretty open and honest. I suffer from anxiety. I've had a little bit of a difficult time over the last six months. I left a previous employer and it didn't go down very well and we had a bit of a court battle and it's not been great. And it's really brought up this condition of mine and made the anxiety ten times worse. I have very, very strange dreams about bad things going to happen to me. Like end of the world. Or just thoughts of dread. The weirdest dream I've had recently was that I literally woke up believing that I couldn't speak or walk. And it was one of those dreams where it was so real that I was trying to wake myself up from it and I could see that I was dreaming and I could feel I was dreaming but I just couldn't actually wake myself up.

Your mind's always creating other things for you to worry about. Which is one of the most difficult things. You get over a worry but then your mind creates another worry. And funnily enough, a psychiatrist was telling me the story why. He says, if you can imagine the UK at the moment, it's always on high terror alert, so we're always prepared for the eventuality that something's going to happen. He says your brain's exactly the same, the brain's always constantly giving you things to worry about because it's always on high alert so you're able to be prepared to deal with an actual emergency. Even though you may not have any crises in life, your mind creates one in order to keep you constantly on high alert. You're never able to sort of just let things relax and have no crises in your life. Because your mind creates one on purpose to give you that sense.

7.

I was actually in Army. Come out of Army, suffered from PTSD, depression, had a nervous breakdown and when I come round I had all tattoos on my face.

I did, yeah. I went to Iraq and Afghan. Horrible. Well, I enjoyed it in a weird way. I'd do it again. Yeah, absolutely.

Officially, six years but I was recovering because I got injured for eighteen months.

Afghan.

We got ambushed and a bomb went off near me. Obviously I've still got all my ligaments but it shattered me bones. All on me left side, so I got like, I dunno if you can see, me hand's come away there. Me hand and all of me left arm.

There's still a counsellor I can go and see if I want to, but it's always me making the effort and that, so I don't. I'm alright now. This happened a long time ago.

Me cousin, he died the same ambush as I was in. So yeah, I'm lucky, really.

I lost a lot of friends out there, yeah.
Unfortunately.

I tried killing myself. I tried hanging myself after I come out. It actually helped with my PTSD because I've got brain damage to me memory, so I can't remember a lot of me time in the Army, do you know what I mean? It kinda worked, kinda helped in a way, yeah! [laughs] I was hanging for that long that I damaged me memory.

In a way it's helped me! When I meet up with old mates from Army they're telling me stories and I can't remember, even though I was there! I can't even remember me soldier number. Every, every ex-forces, it's er… you remember that.

I was Green Jackets. We went in together. He was a year older. He waited for me to go in, so I could leave school. It's all we wanted to do when we were growing up. Then he come out for a bit, did IT, got an IT job for about nine months, and he hated it, so he went back in and six months later he was in Afghan with us again.

Yeah, it's shit.

Yeah, I'm quite lucky in a way. You see like homeless people, ex-forces—I can't get me head round that. When you give your life to the country, literally their life. And then they can't even get a roof over their head. It just seems madness to me. So as I say, I'm quite fortunate.

9.

That's it, see. That's why you can't take no one at face value. You do that, and you know, we've seen people in the past where you'd imagine that they're nothing like what they look like. They might look like summat you'd never ever take 'em for. Then when you get speaking to them you realise that, you know, actually it changes your perception on life.

They say don't judge a book by its cover, though.

That's it, yeah.

Don't judge a book by its cover.

One of our mates is an ex-SAS sniper. And you'd never ever see it—you know, brilliant, absolutely lovely person. That's it.

This time probably thirty years ago probably you'd have a lot of people stop. Without a doubt. Whereas now, how many people have drove past?

That's it.

•

1.

[Laughs] I met her in 1984, on an Adventure Island holiday in the Inner Hebrides in Scotland. She was 13, I was 14. Or she was 12 and I was 13, something like that. And we got on really well. There was a group of us on that holiday. And me and Rebecca stayed in touch as pen pals for years. We met up again when we were about eighteen or nineteen, I think, in London, just for the day. Then I went off to A and university and all the rest of it and we sort of lost touch. And then about ten years ago, I suppose, Rebecca contacted me on Facebook. And we started sharing what was going on in our lives and all the rest of it. At the time, I was still married, she was married as well. We just kept abreast of what was going on in each other's lives. I knew about her marriage breakup and she knew about mine, she knew about me going into acting and I thought, *I'm down in London now so we should meet up.* So we did. And yeah, it was like, *Oh my god—I never found you attractive twenty, thirty years ago, what the hell's going on?!* So yeah, it's really good, it's really, really nice...

2.

I think the first thing that we really need to do is get the kids into school, to get them settled. And also the wife's got to be the priority because she's sacrificed so much. I mean, me, I would happily do anything, whether it's pick fruit in fields or dig up potatoes or work on some building site. I would do anything. But ideally I'd like to do something that involves giving something back. You know, I had some amazing experiences over the last year with plant medicine and... I've had my consciousness expanded.

Okay, well there's quite a lot of different

sorts of plant medicines. There's things like, I dunno if you've heard of ayahuasca?

So, there's one called bufo alvarius. Now bufo alvarius is the Sonorian desert frog. And this particular frog stays underground for nine months of the year, comes out for three months, mates and then goes back under. But in its glands it has something—and it's the only animal that contains this—and it's called a 5 MeO-DMT. The God Molecule. Where ayahuasca gives you like different psychedelic experiences, the frog medicine, the toad medicine, doesn't give you the psychedelics, but it does give you a much more spiritual experience. It sort of opened up my eyes to who I am and what life is all about. Well, not necessarily what life is all about, but just how insignificant we are as human beings. And it kinda fills your heart with a lot of love.

This was a ceremony in London. It was run by a particular shaman and I have to say he was really good. I mean, there's quite a strict procedure with regards to fasting and making sure that you're well prepared and that the setting is exactly as it should be. Actually next week I'm going to another ceremony but it's not a bufo, it's a fire and cacao ceremony.

Basically like chocolate medicine. Cacao. It's basically chocolate. It opens up your heart and it just expands your consciousness and you know, opens your heart to love.

I didn't do this lightly. This has been something which I've been interested in for a number of years. You do your research and you wait for your calling. And my calling came earlier this year.

3.

To be honest I used to travel all over with building and I always picked up the blokes that deliver the lorries and all that. Like the plates and all that. Because I was on me own driving so it was just someone to talk to. It don't bother me. If someone wants a lift it's fine.

You don't see the blokes with plates anymore. In the last two years I don't think I've seen any really.

6.

I play a bit of guitar but not really. Roofing takes it out of your hands so much, so it's not much good really. Everything's aching.

7.

We've only just started living together, which is why I've got the satnav on to get to hers.

Facebook, actually.

Yeah, a bit strange actually.

People post all their personal stuff, don't they,
which I don't understand.

Then they moan when people butt in their lives.
I'm like, *Well stop writing your personal shit then!*
Then you're not giving anyone the chance.

It's crazy, isn't it?

I dunno if she added me or I added her. I can't
remember. We've been Friends for a while
but we just never spoke. And then actually,
on Suggested Friends, she come up under a
different name. So I messaged her, cos she was
saying she had trouble with an ex-boyfriend
and blah blah blah. So I messaged her to
see if she's got another account or if it's her
boyfriend, trying to add folk and whatnot.

And she said she had and we just got talking from there.

Yeah, she's an hairdresser. An hairdresser and nail tech. She's self-employed, she's like mobile and stuff. So she can pick and choose what hours she does. She's got kids so it works for her with school runs and stuff.

8.

It's a strange scenario. It's one of those, where you get made redundant and you never think it's gonna happen to you. And when you do, you kind of become bitter and have to start again. But you have to wipe the redundancy out your head a little bit because if you take it to interviews you're gonna struggle.

It happens. It's business at the end of the day.

My old man, as well as having the shop, he

used to work for British Railways. So he had an apprenticeship in train engineering and design. He did that pretty much for forty odd years and then same thing happened, he got made redundant. But thankfully Dad went into contracting afterwards, which worked out better for him, in terms of money, but in terms of experience as well. He worked on a lot more different projects. And it took him a lot further. And actually it secured him financially as well.

9.

I'd say it comes from the media. Cos the media likes separation, likes segregation. They try and control who does what, who speaks to who. Like racism. Racism's mainly now because of the media. Cos where we live it's very multicultural. And you get the media that's trying to split yous up. End of the day, our landlord, he's Asian, and we live in area where there's a lot of Asians, but it depends how they're brought up as well. Because some of those Asians, they're brought up to hate Whites. Whereas, we've been brought up, you respect and you treat how you wanna be tret.

•

2.

You'd probably call it a midlife crisis!

You kind of wonder, *Who am I? Where am I going? What is life all about?* And I'm certainly at that kind of stage. But what bufo has done to me, it's opened a door. It doesn't cure anything but it opens a door and shows you a light and then you make your own choices. But the ego is a strong thing. So dissolution of that ego is something which certainly one session wasn't enough. I've had two separate ceremonies earlier this year. I went much,

much deeper on the last session. My first session really was just all about ecstasy and beauty—I didn't meet my demons. Where in the last session, I met my demons. Not that you can put it into any kind of words. There are no words for it. To be able to articulate what happened on that day, there are no words to express it. But it's something that I'm so glad that I've done.

I feel like a soul in a shell. You know? And this is just an opportunity for my soul to express itself and feel something tangible. I mean, my mother died of cancer earlier in March, after a ridiculously short battle. Diagnosed and dead within eleven weeks. And I think what that really did for me was it gave me some comfort. If I can try and articulate it in some way, when you smoke this bufo, you fall back and you just feel that every atom, every particle of your body just disappears. You become part of the universe. I felt this real comfort. It took away any fear of death that I may have had. [laughs] I mean, of course, I've got my two children. I wouldn't like them to come home to find out that Daddy's been stabbed and robbed and dead, but yeah... Also it gave me a feeling that I know my mother is in a beautiful place and she's gone back to source and, you know, I feel the same way. I feel that the time I have left on this planet that I wanna do everything I can to be good, to take care of whatever I can, to be good to people, to be good to myself. You know, to learn to love yourself. You can't really love other people until you really learn how to love yourself. There's still a lot of questions. I've not finished by a long shot!

3.

I've just found out, bloke I used to play cricket with, he's just died at 51. Heart attack. And he never drinked, smoked, did nothing. Young kids, or youngish, like. Yeah, real shock. I'd lost a bit of contact with him but I just found out he's died back in August, September.

Ah, I packed it in now. I used to play but not anymore.

4.

I've known since I was a child, that there is more, much more to a human being than we envisage in the 3D, as I call it, the three-dimensional journey that we take with other people. The spiritual aspect of the human is largely ignored. I tried to ignore it. My life wasn't going well from the age of about seven to fifty. I'd put myself and my inner needs on the shelf for forty years. And it wasn't until I started to try and release them that I realised that the feelings I had were also connected to my mental health challenges.

I'd suffered from depression for a long time. I'd also had, intermittently, psychotic episodes that I now understand are born out of not living in the right mind and body space. That came about through needing to understand my own journey. And that took a lot of work, that took a lot of courage, that nearly ended my existence completely. All I had to do was relinquish control of myself to that spiritual entity and surrender. Once I'd done that, the whole of me changed. And I now live, for the past two years, in *my whole self.*

5.

There's not a lot of stuff that you can do about it to be fair. You've gotta sort of try and rationalise it yourself. Speaking to people about it really helps, getting your feelings out and talking to others. I try and play a lot of sports. I play a lot of tennis and things like that just to try and calm me mind and whatnot.

But yeah, it's just really, really difficult. You've got to try and keep yourself busy. And in my job it's difficult because I spend so much time driving, things just pop into my head for no particular reason whatsoever. And then you're sitting on your own rethinking about it, rethinking about it. And the craziest thing about it is you're always questioning everything you do when you've got anxiety.

I've tried to seek help for it, of course. The counsellor has given me techniques of being able to try and clear my mind. One of the techniques works something on the lines of, imagine you've got a bubble and in that bubble you've got all your worries in life. You put everything inside that bubble. You blow the bubble up until the point that the bubble pops and when it pops everything in there just gets destroyed. And he says, *Just imagine, that is your troubles.* And he says if you ever get into this thing where you can't rationalise things and you can't calm yourself down, just take a step, sit down, pull over, think of the bubble, close your eyes. You try it and you feel like a silly sod to start with, but it actually does work. I think it's just a way of calming your mind. It doesn't make your troubles go away, it just helps calm your mind.

6.

We go to H____ G____ in N__________, me and my mate, and there's sweet shops with two tables, so you sit down and just have a bit of curry and fresh naans are absolutely gorgeous for like three quid. It's ridiculous.

It's the staple diet now of the Brits isn't it?

Well they're saying the tikka masala is British, aren't they? They're saying that was invented in Birmingham, aren't they? Things change and evolve, anyway, don't they? Everything does. You know, using different meats and stuff—I mean you don't get many goat curries over here, do you? It's all chicken and beef.

7.

I always knew even from being 5, 6, I just wanted to go in Army. I never thought I'd have to leave the Army. I always thought I'd either retire there or it'd kill me. So I weren't bothered about me GCSEs or nothing like that.

Getting used to civvy street, I think. When you're getting told when you've got to eat, when you go to toilet, everything, to ever be on your own devices, it's a bit strange. You get used to a routine. And I weren't in Army that long to be fair. I know people who've been in there twenty years. So it must be harder for them coming out.

Yeah, completely different. But you get used to it. In time, like. Can't get a decent job, cos I messed around with me GCSEs and stuff like that, but yeah…

I wouldn't change it. No, I wouldn't change anything. I'd go back in now if I could. Yeah, absolutely. Hopefully me kids go in. I'd love it.

•

1.

B____ T_____'s actors studio. He specialises in Method acting. He's one of the only teachers in the UK who specialises in Method Acting. It was great fun. My God, it was a challenge. Holy shit! But yeah, really, really, really good fun.

You know, you learn so much about who you are that you've buried for so many years.

Cos we're conditioned to have that stiff upper lip and not to show certain emotions or to be a certain way.

And acting is all about getting rid of all those things and being someone else, for a time. So yeah, it's a really interesting, intense way of learning how to act. And it's definitely not for everybody! [laughs]

Some of the people on the course really got into the Method way of doing it. I didn't. But there was definitely lots of things from it that I learnt that I will continue to use in my career. Although I've done a Method Acting course, I wouldn't class myself as a Method Actor by any stretch of the imagination. But I am Method-trained, I suppose.

Use what works for you, that's the most important thing.

2.

The thing is I am psychologically addicted to marijuana, because you know it really changed me as a kid. I was a highly strung, boisterous young lad and every time I drunk alcohol I'd always end up in some fight or some row or some stupid kind of thing which caused me no end of trouble. And you know, once I found marijuana it changed me as a person, it calmed me down and made me a better person. And you know, to be honest with you, since my mum got diagnosed with the cancer—and then there was nothing that the hospital can do—I mean, I immediately went on the research and I was getting hold of cannabis oil with 85% THC in it and trying to do anything I could to save my mum. Which was pretty much in vain. But you know cannabis is perhaps on one of the lower levels of a psychedelic and, although it gets such a really bad reputation, I think it can be for anything. I mean, I don't smoke a bag of weed a night. I roll a joint, that joint will last me two to three days, cos I only need like three to four puffs, just to kind of give me that release in the shoulders.

4.

Yeah, very specific indeed. And I don't mind you asking. I was sexually abused from the age of 7 to 15—and that was what had always been the shame around who I was and what I was trying to hide. It is a really significant part of the journey, because what happened at that point was that I separated myself from my own childhood. At that point, I became two different people.

If you talk to a child, they accept you for who you are, they feel you for who you are. They only have fears and conditions around their personality that are placed there by other people. They don't have the barriers until someone creates them—or an event creates them. People are shaped by experience. And obviously every single one of our experiences, together with our natural genetic personality, is completely and utterly unique.

But I hadn't realised that separation had happened, that I'd been detached from my own natural feelings and development as a child. So part of my journey in mental health was having to go back to that point where I was separated, in order to become the whole that I am now. Because I hadn't realised for forty years that I was two separate people. And once I'd reconnected with that child everything just fell into place.

There is no real plan. I think sometimes when we plan, we create our own borders, we create restrictions and/or expectations that we may or may not be able to meet. I think planning is a form of control and I think losing the

3D—in inverted commas—control takes you to a higher place where you don't feel the need anymore. And that is where you go with the flow. That is the spiritual side. I'm just gonna let my journey shape itself. And that's where I'm at. So I don't really have any plans.

5.

I think I've always been on the border of having a condition. But I think with the sort of things that have happened over the last six months and the extra worry within my life, it's sort of put me over the line and made me go seek some help. I was always the type of person that thought mental conditions were all in your head, which [laughs] is obvious! They are all in your head, of course! But I used to think if you say you're suffering from depression or anxiety, *Pull yourself together, will you?* Until you suffer from it yourself and you realise actually it is a condition. I can't describe how it makes me feel, and there is no physical reason for it to make me feel that way. It just does. But I'd always had a worrying sort of mind. And I'd always had a mechanical type of mind. I have to rationalise everything. When I get on a plane, for example, I have to know the type of plane I'm on and know the procedure of it taking off and landing. And I think a lot of it is a control aspect. I do a lot of racing, I race cars, I like to do go-karting and stuff of that nature. And I like to go super fast speed. But that's because I'm in control. If you put me in the passenger seat I hate it. I can't stand it. I don't want to be anywhere near it. Being the passenger and being out of control, it doesn't sit well with me.

7.

I've got five. But she's got four, so I suppose it's nine altogether. So it's busy. My oldest is 15 at the moment, and my youngest is 2. Well, 2 and a half, she's nearly 3. But hers are 14, the youngest is 4, nearly 5. It's a busy time, yeah.

Me youngest don't cos me youngest is in Thailand. Her mum's Thai, like.

Yeah. I Facetime her a couple of times a day and stuff. And I go out three or four times a year, whenever I get a chance.

I split up from me wife and four days later I went to Thailand with the lads, as you do, and met her. And got her pregnant straight away. And yeah, we never really had a relationship or anything like that. But I got a daughter out on it so it's all good.

I know, I've been married three times, I have. Yeah, married and divorced three times. Five kids with four different women.

8.

No. So my dad came over when he was seven with my grandparents. He married my mum when he was twenty, which was an arranged marriage. Mum came over from India. And been happy ever after.

I've done quite well over the last few years. Progressed quite quickly, so this redundancy's kinda come as a shock, but you just crack on, don't you? Just crack on.

I'm getting married this year.

Thank you. However, I can see my bank balance depleting very, very quickly, so the need for a new job is quite, is quite... yeah, it's quite a big need. But it's getting there. It's one of those where there's a low point and you have to get back up.

I met her through friends. We took quite a traditional route, actually, that we only met like a year ago. As Indians, there's two ways of doing it. You can either fall in love and go the long distance relationship, or you can get introduced, have a chat, have a few dates, and pretty much close to the time know she's the one. And that's what happened with us. After the sixth, seventh date, we pretty much went, *Right—I think you're the one.* It's quite interesting that a lot of people that get married that have been in love or whatever, had a long relationship, within three years or two years of getting married they get divorced. While, if you think about the old, traditional ways where, for my parents for instance, they're an arranged marriage. And they're still married fifty years down the line.

Yeah, it's an exciting time at the moment. Busy, hectic, scary, but…

Very big, yeah.

Need to feed five hundred people, somehow!

9.

She's the one who has all the dreams. What dreams have you had, Pip? She wakes up every morning and tells me she's had a dream. One of them was a lion, was he eating us?

No, no, a fox was eating you, Jenny, Lianne and...

Dada and Nana had to come and rescue you.

•

2.

I'm actually preparing myself at the moment, psychologically, for the recommended

Psilocybin dose, which is the 5 gram Psilocybin, which actually takes you on to that real level of er, of er, of er, I don't know. I just don't know! But I know it's gonna take me…

…to the next level, yeah. That's the problem when people take mushrooms and stuff—they're not taking enough of a dose. You've gotta get the dosage right. So I'm taking the Terence McKenna recommended dose of mushrooms.

Well *that*—is five grams.

Gonna eat them, yeah.

Start at eight, you know. Gotta get your setting right, so you don't eat for six hours before and then, darkened room, no music, couple of joints rolled. Because apparently, if you need to change direction within a trip, then the cannabis will change direction for you. So if you're not enjoying what's happening, then, yeah, there's various tips and stuff.

Yes. I mean my sister will be my trip-sitter for me. Making a lot of confessions here! [laughs]

3.

How far north are you hoping to get today then?

Bloody hell, that's a fair old bit of travelling isn't it?

I could never move back down. I wouldn't want to move back down. I'm happy enough with what I'm doing now.

4.

No, it's absolutely fine and I don't have a problem with that. That was a really important part of my own journey, because I never told that story until about four years ago. I chose by not saying it out loud to be the victim. A lot of people do that. I'm saying it doesn't define me—but it does define my experience, growing up and not being able to become a fully emotionally-balanced adult. But also, you know, if you want to you can put in the fact that, what didn't help that journey was my father's suicide when I was 17 years old, when he was 38, and then, three years later, my older brother's suicide at the age of 22 when I was 21. So when you put that into the mix of what my family had already determined their tragic existence was gonna be, now you can see how important it was for me to break that cycle.

5.

One of each. One of each. Boy's the eldest, girl's the youngest. Boy turns 16 this year, girl turns 13. And obviously we were young parents. Had me first child at twenty.

Well I'm always worried. [laughs] I'm always worried about the future, present, past, but I think it's gonna be very difficult for the next generation, especially my kids. Getting on in the property ladder is becoming impossible in certain circumstances. The amount of deposit you've got to get together now and the house prices etcetera. We're reasonably lucky in the location we are—N_________ and above is sort of relatively reasonable price. But obviously living in London and places like that, I really don't know how anybody is ever going to get onto the property ladder living in that area. Obviously money and things like that, that's obviously going to be an issue for the kids. And they seem to have lost—and again my kids certainly have—they've lost that get up and go. I can't get my kids out of the house. I always say that if we ever had a zombie apocalypse, I would survive it because I've got the knowhow and the ability to fend

for myself. And if I have to go live in the
woods to avoid getting eaten I'll probably do
it. Where my kids'd turn around and say, *Is
there an app to do that?*

*Is there an app that's going to allow me to
survive the zombie apocalypse? And what do
I do if my phone runs out of charge?* I don't
think their mother helps them if I'm honest.
She mollycoddles them. I don't think we're
in a different world, I just think it's more
prominent now. My generation, things
were happening but you weren't really seeing
them. Where now everything's in the public
eye and obviously you can't look at a child
these days without obviously being accused of
something. And I think our kids have lost a little
bit. Like going out at 9 o'clock in the morning
and your parents didn't worry about you until
tea time. My mum always used to say, *Oh, don't
worry, he'll be back when his stomach's rumbling.* And

they'd never worry about you all day. You'd be in a mate's house or you'd be out playing football somewhere or whatever. Where now I don't let my kids stay at anybody's house until I've physically vetted them and make sure that they're sound people and I know what the dad does and the mum does and things like that.

Really, really, really, really strange to be fair.

7.

I'm a Christian, so yeah.

I've always believed but I just didn't really give a damn. Then I become a Christian, I think it were 2009. 2009/2010 time?

Yeah, Church of England, yeah.

If I'm not working I'll go, yeah.

I believe in Heaven. I don't really believe in Hell if I'm honest. I suppose they could go hand in hand but... I believe everyone goes to Heaven. That's what I believe. God's forgiving in't he?

There's got to be more to life than this, hasn't there? You'd've thought?

Yeah, we hope so! [laughs]

I was actually in prison and I don't know why, I just had an urge to start reading the Bible. Never had it before. And it just went from there. Strange really.

I never thought I'd be sat reading a Bible, but it happened.

Yeah, well there's chapel, where you can go to on a Sunday, and you can speak to the priest there. You make an appointment but, yeah, you can speak to him and that.

I think it has, because I doubted meself a lot more. I don't know how to explain it. You question yourself to make sure it's the right thing or not. I've got a conscience now. I never really did. Well, I probably did, I probably just didn't listen to it!

8.

No, I'm religious at the same time. I'm Sikh so there has to be a point of religion in that. I have my beliefs.

I'm a logical thinker, but a believer.

My decisions are always logical and always are made with the long term in mind. Short, sharp decisions are fine but I will always look at the longer term vision. Hence why I don't really give a shit about the small decisions or the smaller things in life. As long as it comes eventually it doesn't really bother me.

Reincarnation.

It's how you lived your life. If you been good or bad then you go lower down the pecking order basically. And that is reincarnation. So you might've been great in this life, and you'll be like king in the next, or [a] wealthy person or whatever, unlucky person or however you wanna see it. It all depends on how you've been in your current life. Or your past.

Yeah, yeah—it's constant evolution.

9.

We end up doing a lot for memories. Like this now. This is gonna go down with us as another memory, do you know what I mean? Straight away…

We just like memories, don't we?

That's what we're about. We collect memories. Certain places we go to. It's like, we love travelling, absolutely love it, and we love meeting new people, so this is best of the best, this.

That's it.

We're meeting somebody now who's writing a book!

So what got you into writing?

•

2.

I mean, we live in an idyllic little village at the moment, which has got great state schools, full facilities and stuff. But it's just a life of consumption. And my daughters are now getting into devices and stuff, and I can see how quickly they're becoming addicted to those devices. I'm driving a car, I'm putting a thousand pounds worth of fuel in the car every month, which I'm dumping as CO_2 into the environment. And I just don't feel like I'm doing something positive. And obviously with the mortgage and having a single salary coming in for the last nine years, it means in fact I've spent money that I haven't got. I've got money on credit cards, loans and stuff, keeping things going, always imagining that the wife's gonna go back to work pretty soon and she's struggled with getting back to work and we're just very fortunate that we have a pretty low mortgage and a property which is in high demand, where we could make an absolute fortune, so we can basically clear our debts.

It's a complete change of life. And hopefully,

something that's gonna take us a little bit out of our comfort zone.

Exactly. And you know, they've still got grandparents that live in X. I mean, her dad had a heart attack a few weeks ago, he had a stroke a number of years ago, so it'll be really nice to be close to the family and give them the joy of the grandchildren and also in some ways pre-empt what may or may not happen in the course of the next three, four, five, six, ten years, who knows? If one of the in-laws would pass away, then the wife'd wanna go back to X and she wouldn't just wanna go and take a funeral and say, *Right, we're off now.* So, although that's a very difficult conversation to have, it's still a practicality which should be considered. So if we were gonna do something like that, now's the right time. Before my oldest gets into secondary education. Gives her a time to adjust and bed in. So I think timing is everything and that opportunity is here and now.

3.

I used to pick up the old army boys going back to the barracks and all that as well. That's another thing. You don't see that anymore either.

4.

And that's where I'm saying the will and the determination to not be subjected to external experiences is where the spiritual aspect of us lies. So many allow themselves to be the victim that is destroyed by experience. A lot of people that are really spiritually-inclined will tell you that we shape our own experiences all round. That's a bitter pill to swallow! Because that means in a way we've created our own tragedies. That's quite high-up thinking, that's a bitter pill for most people. *Oh don't be ridiculous, I didn't ask for that.* The way that you naturally and automatically want to blame somebody else for something is where the victim mentality comes from.

And I know that I don't need to blame anybody for anything. It all just happened and I'm the person who had to weather that storm. And I did and it's not a badge of honour, it's just me wanting to be who I was all along, and whole. And balanced. And now I feel I've achieved that and that makes me really happy. That's where my joy comes from.

6.

So what's your name? I don't know your name.

7.

We're not far from the junction, I don't believe.

I couldn't tell you, mate, if I'm honest. I just follow satnav nowadays—you don't need a map!

Afterword

In September 2018 I began hitchhiking again, for the first time in almost thirty years. Partly, I wondered whether you still could. When I drove, I no longer saw hitchers—who used to swarm at motorway junctions and service stations—and I was curious whether this was because people could no longer be bothered to thumb it (Megabuses being so cheap) or because no one would pick them up. But I was also developing an idea involving collage, chance, direct reported speech and something I didn't yet dare put into words. In particular, I was attracted by the notion that not only would the project consist of my interviewees' words rather than mine, but my interviewees would choose me, too. This seemed somehow important, thought I couldn't—can't—say why.

On Tuesday May 21st 2019, I travelled from Redbridge in East London up the M11, then the A1(M) past Newark, across to the M1 just below Sheffield, before heading South and eventually abandoning hope of a lift at Donnington Park services, having been moved off junction 24 by the police. At the time of writing, this is also the last of my hitching expeditions. I can't explain why, just that it's an ending of sorts (though a slightly unsatisfactory one). In presenting this text I've changed the names of all contributors, and everyone they mentioned, and disguised place names. Although everyone gave me permission to use their words, these were decisions taken in a moment, while a stranger sat in their vehicle, and I don't want to get anyone into trouble.

Transcripts are edited, truncated and, to some extent, manipulated, but the contributors are numbered according to the order I met them in. My words are represented by blank lines. For obvious reasons, you don't tend to get many lifts from lone women when hitching, so when Kirsten followed me on social media, a day or two after my excursion, I was quick to contact her and ask her if she would speak to me again, this time over the phone. Hence, her interview is taken both from the five minutes we spent together in her car and our later conversation.

Acknowledgements

Thanks first and foremost to the generosity of the people who gave me lifts and then shared their lives with me.

Thanks to Leila Baker, Max Porter and, in particular, Sean Preston, for help with the text.

'Not Far From The Junction' forms part of an ongoing, multi-piece non-fiction project, *Your Words Never Mine.*
www.yourwordsnevermine.net